C000143005

SPC INTERNATIONAL

ACA SPECIALIST CONTRACT FOR PROJECT

SPECIALIST AGREEMENT

A SPECIALIST CONTRACT is made the _____ day of _____   _____

IN RELATION TO _____

_____ (the "Specialist Works")

forming part of _____ (the "Project")

at _____ (the "Site")

BETWEEN the Constructor and the Specialist who have executed this Specialist Agreement

WHO AGREE working in mutual cooperation to fulfil their agreed roles and responsibilities and apply their agreed expertise in relation to the Specialist Works, in accordance with and subject to the Specialist Documents as each defined below, and that subject to amendment in accordance with the Specialist Terms:-

Reference in Specialist Terms

Clause 1.1   The Specialist Works, the Project and the Site are further described in the Specialist Documents.

Clause 1.2   The procurement of the Project is governed by a project partnering contract based on the PPC International ACA Standard Form of Contract for Project Partnering dated _____ _____ (the "Partnering Contract") and entered into between _____

_____ (the "Client"), the Constructor and others (together the "Partnering Team").

(Delete if not applicable)   The Specialist has executed the Partnering Contract or has executed or shall execute (within ten (10) Working Days from the date of its receipt) a Joining Agreement in the form set out in the Partnering Contract completed in conformity with the Specialist Documents and is or shall become (upon executing a Joining Agreement) a Partnering Team member.

(Delete italics as appropriate)   The Specialist has been provided with *a copy of the Partnering Contract/the following parts of the Partnering Contract*:-

_____

_____

_____

Clause 1.3   The roles, expertise and responsibilities of the Constructor and the Specialist are further described in the Specialist Documents and the Specialist shall be paid in accordance with the Specialist Terms and the Specialist Payment Terms.

Clause 2

The Specialist Documents (subject to addition and amendment in accordance with the Specialist Terms) shall comprise the following:-

▶ this Specialist Agreement and the Specialist Terms;

▶ the Specialist Works Brief comprising:-

_____

_____

▶ the Specialist Works Proposals comprising:-

_____

_____

▶ the Specialist Timetable;

▶ any Commencement Notices;

▶ the Specialist Payment Terms set out in:-

_____

▶ *the Specialist KPIs set out in:-*

_____

▶ *the Partnering Contract/the following parts of the Partnering Contract:-*

_____

_____

▶ *the following other Specialist Documents:-*

_____

_____

Clause 5.6

The Client Representative is:-

_____

Clause 6.1

The Specialist Timetable is set out as follows in this Specialist Agreement and *is/is not* further detailed in *a separate Specialist Timetable/the Specialist Works Brief.*

Clauses 6.1 and
15.1

▶ Implementation of all or each stated stage of the Specialist Works shall commence within the following periods from the date of each of the following Commencement Notices which, subject to the Specialist Terms, the Constructor shall issue no earlier or later than the following earliest and latest dates:-

Stage of Specialist Works	Period after Commencement Notice	Earliest Date	Latest Date
_____	_____	_____	_____
_____	_____	_____	_____
_____	_____	_____	_____
_____	_____	_____	_____

SPC INTERNATIONAL   © ACA and Trowers & Hamlins 2007

Clauses 6.1, 8.1,
8.2, 8.5 and 8.7

(Delete
if not
applicable)

▶ The periods for Constructor provision of designs and other information, for Specialist provision of design submissions/contributions and other information, for Constructor comments, for Specialist re-submissions and for Value Engineering shall be as follows in relation to the following stages of design development:-

_____

_____

_____

_____

_____

Clause 6.1

(Delete
italics as
appropriate)

▶ *The period for procurement/fabrication/delivery to Site shall be* _____

from _____

▶ *The period for implementation on Site shall be* _____

from _____

▶ The Date for Specialist Completion shall be _____

from _____

Clause 6.2

(Delete
if not
applicable)

▶ The Specialist Works are in the following Specialist Sections:-

_____

_____

_____

Clause 6.3

(Delete
italics as
appropriate)

▶ The Constructor's possession of the Site *is exclusive/non-exclusive* and is subject to the following constraints, procedures and arrangements *as further described in the stated other Specialist Documents:-*

_____

_____

_____

_____

Clause 8

(Delete
italics as
appropriate)

The Lead Designer and the Design Team are as stated in the Partnering Contract and the Specialist *is/is not* a member of the Design Team.

Clause 8.2

(Delete
if not
applicable)

The design development process shall be amended as follows:-

_____

_____

_____

Clause 8.3

(Delete
if not
applicable)

The following Site surveys and investigations shall be commissioned or undertaken by the following parties:-

_____

_____

_____

Clause 11.1

(Delete
if not
applicable)

The following Volume Supply Agreements shall be utilised by the Specialist:-

_____

_____

_____

Clause 12

The Specialist Price, as further described in the Specialist Payment Terms, is:-

_____

Clause 13.2

(Delete
if not
applicable)

The shared savings arrangements and/or added value incentives applicable to the Specialist are as follows:-

_____

_____

_____

Clause 14.1

(Delete
if not
applicable)

Implementation of the Specialist Works and issue of any Commencement Notices stated in the Specialist Timetable shall be subject to satisfaction of the following further pre-conditions:-

_____

_____

_____

SPC INTERNATIONAL   © ACA and Trowers & Hamlins 2007

Clause 15.3(v)

(Delete
if not
applicable)

Risk in the following materials, goods and equipment shall pass to the Constructor on the following dates or events:-

_____

_____

Clause 15.4

(Delete
if not
applicable)

Ownership of the following materials, goods and equipment shall pass to the Constructor on the following dates or events:-

_____

_____

Clause 18

The treatment of risk under clause 18 of the Specialist Terms shall be subject to the following:-

Clause 18.2

Risk sharing arrangements (if any):- _____

_____

_____

Clause 18.3(iii)

Third party consents (if any) entitling a claim for extension of time:- _____

_____

Clause 18.3(xvi)

Additional events (if any) entitling a claim for extension of time:- _____

_____

Clause 18.5

Adjusted extensions of time (if any) entitling a claim for additional Site Overheads:-

_____

Clause 18.6

Adjusted extensions of time (if any) entitling a claim for unavoidable work/expenditure:-

_____

Clause 18.7

Exceptions and clarifications (if any) in respect of Specialist risk as to the Site Environment:-

_____

_____

Clause 19.1   Insurance of the Project and the Site shall be taken out by:-

_____

_____

in the names of:-   _____

_____

With waiver of rights of subrogation against:-   _____

_____

With the following percentage addition for fees:-   _____

_____

With the following additional or adjusted risks (if any):-   _____

_____

_____

Clause 19.1   Insurance (if any) of third party property damage shall be taken out by:-

_____

in the following amount:-   _____

Clauses 19.3 and 19.4   The amounts of third party liability insurance and professional indemnity insurance/product liability insurance of the Specialist shall be:-

Third Party Liability   **Professional Indemnity**   **Product Liability**

_____

Clause 19.9

(Delete if not applicable)

The amount and form of any Specialist advance payment guarantee/performance bond/ parent company guarantee/retention bond shall be:-

_____

_____

_____

Clause 20.2   The date for commencement of the first interval until a payment application is submitted shall be:-

_____

Clause 20.3
(Delete if not applicable)

The revised period for issue of valuations shall be:-   _____

_____

Clause 20.3
(Delete if not applicable)

The revised period for payment shall be:-   _____

_____

SPC INTERNATIONAL   © ACA and Trowers & Hamlins 2007

Clause 20.8 The rate of interest on late payment shall be:- _____

_____

Clause 20.11
(Delete
if not
applicable) The revised period for issue of an account following Specialist Completion shall be:-

_____

Clause 20.12 The Specialist Final Account shall be issued within twenty (20) Working Days from:-

_____

Clause 21.4 The Specialist Defects Liability Period shall be:-

_____

Clause 21.4 The time limits for rectification of defects shall be:-

_____

_____

_____

Clauses 22.1 and
22.4
(Delete
if not
applicable) The following amended duties of care, warranties and third party rights shall apply:-

_____

_____

Clause 22.2

(Delete
if not
applicable) The following direct agreements shall be provided:- _____

_____

_____

Clause 25.2
(Delete
if not
applicable) The following rights of assignment shall apply:- _____

_____

Clauses 25.4 and
27.6 The applicable law and the courts with jurisdiction shall be those of:- _____

_____

Clause 27.3 Under the Specialist Problem-Solving Hierarchy each of the following individuals shall have a period of _____ (___) Working Days to agree a solution with the individual stated opposite his or her name, failing which the notified Specialist difference or dispute shall be referred to the next named individuals (if any):-

Constructor	**Specialist**
1. _____	_____
2. _____	_____
3. _____	_____

Clause 27.4 and
Appendix 4
Part 1
(Delete
if not
applicable)

The Conciliator/Mediator shall be:- _____

_____

and the conciliation/mediation shall be conducted according to the following rules:- _____

_____

Clause 27.5 and
Appendix 4
Part 2

(Delete
if not
applicable)

Any Specialist dispute or difference may be referred to an arbitrator in accordance with the procedure set out in Part 2 of Appendix 4, and as follows:-

► the number of arbitrators shall be:- _____

► in the absence of agreement the appointing authority or equivalent shall be:-

_____

► the arbitration shall be conducted according to the following rules:-

_____

► the location of the arbitration shall be:-

_____

► the language of the arbitration shall be:-

_____

Clause 27.7

The limitation period shall be:-

_____

Clause 28

(Delete
if not
applicable)

The following Specialist Special Terms shall apply:-

_____

_____

_____

_____

_____

_____

SPC INTERNATIONAL © ACA and Trowers & Hamlins 2007

_____ of/whose registered office is at

_____

and of fax number _____ and e-mail address _____

(the "**Constructor**")

SIGNED for and on behalf of the
Constructor by

_____

Name   _____

Title   _____

In the presence of:

_____

_____

_____ of/whose registered office is at

_____

and of fax number _____ and e-mail address _____

(the "**Specialist**")

SIGNED for and on behalf of the
Specialist by

_____

Name   _____

Title   _____

In the presence of:

_____

_____

SPC INTERNATIONAL   © ACA and Trowers & Hamlins 2007

SPC
INTERNATIONAL

SPECIALIST CONTRACT
FOR
PROJECT PARTNERING

SPECIALIST TERMS

SPECIALIST TERMS

CONTENTS

SPC INTERNATIONAL   © ACA and Trowers & Hamlins 2007

SPECIALIST TERMS

1. SPECIALIST WORKS AND PROJECT

Specialist Contract 1.1 The Specialist Contract relates to the Specialist Works, the Project and the Site as each identified in the Specialist Agreement to which these Specialist Terms refer and is made between the Constructor and the Specialist.

Partnering Contract 1.2 The Partnering Contract relates to the Project and the Site and is made between the Partnering Team members and its status in relation to the Specialist Contract is stated in the Specialist Agreement.

Roles and responsibilities 1.3 The Constructor and the Specialist shall work together and individually in the spirit of trust, fairness and mutual cooperation for the benefit of the Specialist Works and the Project, within the scope of their agreed roles, expertise and responsibilities as stated in the Specialist Documents.

Specialist Definitions 1.4 All words and expressions used in these Specialist Terms and in the other Specialist Documents shall have the meanings stated in the Specialist Definitions set out in Appendix 1 or (if not in conflict with the Specialist Definitions) the meanings stated in the Partnering Contract and all clause numbers in these Specialist Terms refer to clauses of these Specialist Terms unless stated otherwise.

Reasonableness 1.5 In all matters governed by the Specialist Contract, including without limitation any required notice, request, submission, decision, consent, approval, comment, valuation, agreement, opinion, instruction and other communication and activity, the Constructor and the Specialist shall act reasonably and without delay.

2. SPECIALIST DOCUMENTS

Roles and relationships 2.1 The Specialist Documents describe the roles, expertise and responsibilities of the Constructor and the Specialist and shall govern the relationship between them and the implementation of the Specialist Works and any Specialist Document created or amended in accordance with these Specialist Terms shall be binding on the Constructor and the Specialist.

Signature of Specialist Documents 2.2 Except as otherwise agreed by the Constructor and the Specialist, all Specialist Documents shall be signed and dated by the Constructor and the Specialist for the purpose of identification.

Responsibility for Specialist Documents 2.3 The party who prepares or contributes to any one or more Specialist Documents shall be responsible for the consequences of any error or omission in, or any discrepancy between, such Specialist Documents or its contributions to them, except to the extent of its reliance (if stated in such Specialist Documents) on any contribution or information provided by the other party.

Specialist Documents complementary 2.4 All Specialist Documents shall be treated as complementary and it shall be the duty of the Constructor and the Specialist to warn each other of any error, omission or discrepancy of which they become aware and (within the scope of their agreed roles, expertise and responsibilities) to put forward proposals to resolve any such error, omission or discrepancy fairly and constructively without adversely affecting the agreed cost or time for completion or quality of the Specialist Works or the Project. Any proposal pursuant to this clause 2.4 shall be subject to prior agreement by the Constructor and the Specialist.

Priority of Specialist Documents 2.5 In the event that a discrepancy cannot be resolved in accordance with clause 2.4, and except where a different priority is agreed by the Constructor and the Specialist, and subject to clause 2.6, the priority between the Specialist Documents shall be as follows in descending order:-

    (i)   the Specialist Agreement;

    (ii)   these Specialist Terms;

    (iii)   the Specialist Timetable;

    (iv)   any Commencement Notice(s);

    (v)   the Specialist Works Brief;

    (vi)   the Specialist Works Proposals;

    (vii)   the Specialist Payment Terms;

    (viii)   any Specialist KPIs;

    (ix)   any other Specialist Documents.

Discrepancies with Partnering Contract   2.6   In the event of a discrepancy between the Partnering Contract and the Specialist Contract that cannot be resolved in accordance with clause 2.4, and except whether a different order of priority is agreed by the Constructor and the Specialist, the Specialist Contract shall prevail.

Partnering Contract events   2.7   The Constructor shall notify the Specialist of any date and/or event under the Partnering Contract that is stated in the Specialist Contract to have an effect on the Specialist Contract.

3.   COMMUNICATION AND ORGANISATION

Cooperative exchange of information   3.1   The Constructor and the Specialist shall work together and individually, in accordance with the Specialist Documents, to achieve transparent and cooperative exchange of information in all matters relating to the Specialist Works and to organise and integrate their activities as part of a collaborative team.

Methods of communication   3.2   Except as otherwise agreed in writing, all notices, requests, submissions, decisions, consents, approvals, comments, valuations, agreements, opinions, instructions and other communications between the Constructor and the Specialist shall be in writing by receipted hand delivery or recorded delivery post or fax or (if the Constructor and the Specialist have signed an appropriate procedural agreement) e-mail, in each case effective from the date of its delivery to the address of the relevant party set out in the Specialist Agreement or to such other address as either party shall notify to the other.

Early Warning   3.3   The Constructor and the Specialist shall operate an Early Warning system, whereby each shall notify the other as soon as it is aware of any matter adversely affecting or threatening the Specialist Works or the Project or its own performance under the Specialist Contract, and (within the scope of its agreed role, expertise and responsibilities) shall include in such notification proposals for avoiding or remedying such matter, and within five (5) Working Days from the date of any such notification the Constructor and the Specialist shall meet in accordance with clause 3.4 unless they agree an alternative course of action.

Meetings   3.4   When stated in the Specialist Timetable or when otherwise necessary to facilitate performance of their agreed roles and responsibilities under the Specialist Contract,

SPC INTERNATIONAL   © ACA and Trowers & Hamlins 2007

either the Constructor or the Specialist may call a meeting with the other:-

(i)   by not less than three (3) Working Days notice stating its purpose unless a shorter period of notice is justified by health and safety reasons or other demonstrable emergency;

(ii)   at the Site or another agreed location;

(iii)   at which both parties shall be represented by individuals with appropriate authority;

(iv)   which may also be attended by such other Core Group or Design Team or Partnering Team members and Other Specialists as either the Constructor or the Specialist may notify to the other and arrange.

Secondments and further cooperation   3.5   The Constructor and the Specialist shall implement such secondments, office sharing arrangements and access to each other's computer networks and databases as are stated in the Specialist Documents, subject to clause 25.5 and to signature of appropriate procedural agreements.

Records   3.6   The Constructor and the Specialist shall keep such records of their activities in relation to the Specialist Works as are required by the Specialist Documents and, subject to clause 25.5 and any other constraints stated in the Specialist Documents, each shall permit inspection of its activities and records in relation to the Specialist Works by the other and by any third parties stated in the Specialist Works Brief.

4.   PARTNERING OBJECTIVES

Partnering objectives   4.1   The Constructor and the Specialist shall establish, develop and implement their partnering relationship, within their agreed roles, expertise and resonsiblities and in accordance with the Specialist Documents, with the objectives of achieving for the benefit of the Specialist Works and the Project and for the mutual benefit of the Constructor and the Specialist:-

(i)   trust, fairness, mutual cooperation, dedication to agreed common goals and an understanding of each other's expectations and values;

(ii)   finalisation of the required designs, timetables, prices and supply chain for the Specialist Works;

(iii)   innovation, improved efficiency, cost-effectiveness, lean production and reduction or elimination of waste;

(iv)   completion of the Specialist Works within the agreed time and price and to the agreed quality;

(v)   measurable continuous improvement by reference to the targets described in the Specialist KPIs;

(vi)   commitment to people including staff and the users of the Specialist Works.

(vii)   any other objectives stated in the Specialist Documents.

5. CONSTRUCTOR INSTRUCTIONS

Instructions to Specialist 5.1 The Constructor shall issue such instructions to the Specialist as are necessary to enable the Specialist to implement the Specialist Works in accordance with the Specialist Documents, including as to the opening up for inspection or testing of any part of the Specialist Works and the rectification or replacement at no cost to the Constructor of any designs, works, services, materials, goods or equipment that are defective or otherwise not in accordance with the Specialist Documents.

Objection to instructions 5.2 Subject to clause 5.3, if an instruction issued by the Constructor is contrary to any Specialist Document or otherwise demonstrably not in the best interests of the Specialist Works or the Project, the Specialist shall notify the Constructor within two (2) Working Days from the date of such instruction. Following Consultation between the Constructor and the Specialist with input from other parties as appropriate, to seek to resolve the Specialist's objection, the Constructor shall confirm, amend or withdraw the relevant instruction and the Specialist shall comply with such confirmation, amendment or withdrawal, or within two (2) Working Days from its date shall implement the procedures described in clause 17 or clause 18 or clause 27 if appropriate.

Urgent instructions 5.3 In respect of a Constructor instruction stated to require immediate compliance justified by health and safety reasons or other demonstrable emergency, the Specialist may give Early Warning if appropriate under clause 3.3 but otherwise shall immediately carry out such instruction without notifying an objection under clause 5.2, and only after carrying out such instruction may implement the procedures described in clause 17 or clause 18 if appropriate.

Compliance with instructions 5.4 Subject to clause 5.2, the Specialist shall promptly carry out an instruction of the Constructor that is consistent with the Specialist Documents. If the Constructor has reason to consider that failure to carry out any such instruction shall materially adversely affect the Specialist Works or the Project, and if the Specialist shall not carry out such instruction within four (4) Working Days from the date of a notice from the Constructor under this clause 5.4 repeating the instruction, then the Constructor may pay another party to carry out such instruction and the Specialist shall permit such other party to do so and any consequent cost additional to the Specialist Price shall be borne by the Specialist by payment to the Constructor or deduction from payments otherwise due pursuant to clause 20.

Other parties' instructions 5.5 The Specialist shall not comply with any instruction in relation to the Specialist Works, the Project or the Site issued by any party other than the Constructor and shall notify the Constructor immediately if any such instruction is issued.

Client Representative 5.6 The Client Representative, as named in the Specialist Agreement or as otherwise notified by the Constructor to the Specialist, shall have the role, expertise and responsibilities described in the Partnering Contract, but shall have no role, expertise or responsibilities under the Specialist Contract unless otherwise agreed by the Constructor and the Specialist.

Value Engineering Value Management and Risk Management 5.7 The Constructor shall organise and monitor the contributions of the Specialist to Value Engineering, Value Management and Risk Management exercises in relation to the Specialist Works, as stated in the Specialist Documents and as otherwise agreed by the Constructor and the Specialist.

SPC INTERNATIONAL   © ACA and Trowers & Hamlins 2007

6. SPECIALIST TIMETABLE

Specialist Timetable

6.1 Subject to any agreed preconditions and subject to clauses 17, 18 and 26.8 and 26.9, the Constructor and the Specialist shall undertake their agreed activities in relation to the Specialist Works regularly and diligently in the stages and within the dates and periods stated in or established pursuant to the Specialist Timetable.

Specialist Sections

6.2 If the Specialist Timetable refers to the division of the Specialist Works into Specialist Sections, then (except where expressly stated to the contrary) all references in the Specialist Documents to the Specialist Works, Commencement Notices, Specialist Completion, the Date for Specialist Completion and the Specialist Completion Date and all other provisions of the Specialist Documents shall apply to the whole Specialist Works and to each and any Specialist Section.

Site access and possession

6.3 The Specialist's rights of access to and possession of the Site shall be non-exclusive and the Specialist Timetable shall state whether possession by the Constructor of the Site or any part of it is exclusive or non-exclusive, by reason of third parties in occupation or otherwise, and shall set out the constraints on Site access and possession and the agreed procedures for all required notices and programming of the Specialist Works to take account of these matters, including without limitation any arrangements for deferred possession and interrupted possession of all or any part of the Site.

Acceleration or postponement

6.4 The Constructor may instruct acceleration, postponement or resequencing of any date or period stated in the Specialist Timetable or any constraint on Site possession or access and, subject to clause 5.2, the Specialist shall treat such instruction as a proposed Specialist Change in accordance with clause 17.

Updating Specialist Timetable

6.5 The Specialist shall prepare and submit to the Constructor at the intervals stated in the Specialist Works Brief an updated Specialist Timetable reflecting any agreed adjustment pursuant to these Specialist Terms and such further information as to actual and anticipated progress of the Specialist Works as may be required by the Specialist Works Brief. The receipt or use of any updated Specialist Timetable and other information shall not be evidence of the Constructor's agreement to its contents.

7. HEALTH AND SAFETY, SITE WELFARE AND EMPLOYEES

Health and safety

7.1 The Constructor and the Specialist shall work together and individually within their agreed roles, expertise and responsibilities as stated in the Specialist Documents to achieve the highest possible standards of health and safety in all activities forming part of the Specialist Works, and otherwise affecting the Project and the Site, and shall implement such health and safety and site welfare measures as are described in the Specialist Documents.

Skills, qualifications and experience

7.2 Each of the Constructor and the Specialist shall employ for the purposes of the Specialist Works individuals with the necessary skills, qualifications and experience to fulfil its role, expertise and responsibilities under the Specialist Contract. The removal or replacement by the Specialist of any individual named in the Specialist Documents shall be subject to the restrictions stated in the Specialist Documents.

Responsibility for individuals

7.3 Each of the Constructor and the Specialist shall use reasonable skill and care to ensure that its employees and all other individuals for whom it is responsible shall adhere to the Specialist Contract and each of the Constructor and the Specialist shall be liable to the other for any loss, damage, injury or death caused by the default or negligence of any such employees and other individuals when on Site or otherwise under its control.

Replacement of individuals

7.4 If any individual employed by the Specialist or for whom it is responsible disrupts or otherwise adversely affects the Specialist Works or the Project, then the Constructor may require the exclusion of that individual from the Specialist Works, the Project and the Site and the Specialist shall engage a suitable replacement and notify the Constructor accordingly.

Employment and training initiatives

7.5 The Constructor and the Specialist shall implement together and individually such employment and training initiatives as are described in the Specialist Documents or otherwise agreed between them.

8. DESIGN AND PROCESS DEVELOPMENT

Design and process contributions

8.1 Without limiting any duty of care or warranty described in clause 22, each of the Constructor and the Specialist shall contribute those aspects of the design of the Specialist Works that fall within its role, expertise and responsibilities as stated in the Specialist Documents and shall provide to each other in accordance with the Specialist Timetable such other information as may be stated in the Specialist Documents.

Specialist designs

8.2 As supplemented and amended by the Specialist Agreement, the Specialist Works Brief and the Specialist Works Proposals, all designs agreed to be provided by the Specialist shall be prepared and developed as follows:-

(i) the Specialist shall prepare and submit its designs to the Constructor for approval or comment no later than the end of the periods stated in the Specialist Timetable;

(ii) the Constructor shall respond to the Specialist within the periods stated in the Specialist Timetable following the date of each submission and, if the comments of the Constructor identify any non-compliance with the Specialist Documents, then within the periods stated in the Specialist Timetable the Specialist shall make the necessary adjustments and shall resubmit such designs for approval or comment in accordance with clause 8.2(i);

(iii) where the Specialist has agreed to contribute to any design, then it shall prepare and submit such contributions to the Constructor in accordance with clauses 8.2(i) and 8.2(ii), within the periods stated in the Specialist Timetable.

Surveys and investigations

8.3 The parties stated in the Specialist Agreement shall commission or undertake any Site surveys and investigations stated in the Specialist Agreement and the Specialist (within its agreed role, expertise and responsibilities as stated in the Specialist Documents) shall assist the Constructor in assessing the effect of the results of such surveys and investigations on the Project and the design of the Specialist Works. The Constructor shall instruct any consequent amendments to the designs of the Specialist Works and the Specialist shall amend its designs for the Specialist Works as instructed, for Constructor approval or comment.

Specialist Price and Specialist Budgets

8.4 The Specialist shall undertake its agreed design responsibilities within the Specialist Price and within any Specialist Budgets and shall provide, with all design submissions, updated cost estimates reconciled with the Specialist Payment Terms.

Value Engineering	8.5	The Specialist shall undertake Value Engineering and submit the results to the Constructor in accordance with the Specialist Timetable. Where the results of such Value Engineering are approved by the Constructor, the Constructor shall instruct any consequent amendments to the designs of the Specialist Works and the Specialist shall amend its designs for the Specialist Works as instructed, for Constructor approval or comment.
Approvals and comments	8.6	No approval or comment by the Constructor in respect of any design provided by the Specialist shall in any way relieve or affect the responsibility of the Specialist for that design.
Constructor provision of designs and other information	8.7	The Constructor shall provide to the Specialist in accordance with the Specialist Timetable such designs and other information as are necessary to enable the Specialist to implement the Specialist Works in accordance with the Specialist Documents.
Specialist objection to designs	8.8	If and to the extent that the Specialist has not prepared or contributed to a design and such design is contrary to any Specialist Document or otherwise demonstrably not in the best interests of the Specialist Works or the Project, the Specialist shall notify any objection to such design to the Constructor within four (4) Working Days from the date of provision of such design (or within any other period stated in the Specialist Timetable). Following Consultation between the Constructor and the Specialist and such other parties as either of them may consider appropriate, the Constructor shall confirm, amend or withdraw the relevant design and the Specialist shall accept such confirmation, amendment or withdrawal, or within two (2) Working Days from its date shall implement the procedures described in clause 17 or clause 18 or clause 27 if appropriate.
Designs as Specialist Documents	8.9	All Specialist Works designs provided (and, if so stated, approved) in accordance with this clause 8 shall become part of the Specialist Works Brief (where and to the extent provided by the Constructor) or shall become part of the Specialist Works Proposals (where and to the extent provided by the Specialist), and any subsequent proposed adjustment to any such design shall be subject to clauses 2.3, 2.4, 2.5 and 2.6 or to clause 17 as appropriate.

9. INTELLECTUAL PROPERTY

Non-infringement of Intellectual Property Rights	9.1	Each of the Constructor and the Specialist warrants to the other that no design or document that it prepares and nothing else that it contributes to the Specialist Works shall infringe any Intellectual Property Rights, and undertakes to indemnify the other in respect of any legal liability and related costs arising out of or in connection with any such infringement of any Intellectual Property Rights.
Licence to copy and use	9.2	Each of the Constructor and the Specialist shall retain Intellectual Property Rights in all designs and other documents that it prepares in relation to the Specialist Works, and as beneficial owner grants to the other an irrevocable, non-exclusive, royalty-free licence to copy and use all such designs and documents for any purpose relating to completion and Operation of the Specialist Works and the remainder of the Project, in all cases with the right to transfer and sub-license such rights for the same purposes, and shall ensure that such licence shall have the support of such rights from third parties as are necessary to allow the grant of such licence.

Liability for use of designs and documents	9.3	Neither the Constructor nor the Specialist shall be liable for the use of any design or document that it prepares for any purpose other than that for which it was agreed to be prepared as stated in, or reasonably inferred from, the Specialist Documents.
Ownership of documents	9.4	Subject to the Intellectual Property Rights described in clause 9.2, ownership in all the existing documents and other physical embodiments of designs relating to the Specialist Works shall transfer from the Specialist to the Constructor (or to the Client if the Specialist has executed the Partnering Contract or a Joining Agreement) immediately prior to the Specialist suffering an event as described in clause 26.2 or termination of its appointment for any other reason as described in clauses 26.1, 26.3 or 26.10. In such circumstances the Specialist shall hand over all such documents and designs to the Constructor (or to the Client if the Specialist has executed the Partnering Contract or a Joining Agreement) immediately upon request.

10. SUB-SPECIALISTS

Sub-Specialist appointments	10.1	Any proposed Sub-Specialist appointments shall be subject to prior approval by the Constructor and in all proposed Sub-Specialist appointments the Specialist shall seek to establish relationships that:-

    (i)   are Open-book to the maximum achievable extent;

    (ii)   clearly reflect the agreed requirements of the Constructor, the interests of the Constructor and the Specialist and the needs of the Specialist Works;

    (iii)   secure the best available warranties and support and maximise the potential for innovation and other contributions to the Specialist Works;

    (iv)   establish and demonstrate best value to the Constructor;

    (v)   are, wherever possible, complementary to the relationship described in the Specialist Contract;

    (vi)   incorporate terms consistent with the Specialist Contract, to the extent that these are relevant to the Sub-Specialist's agreed role, expertise and responsibilities.

Responsibility for Sub-Specialists	10.2	The Specialist shall be responsible for all aspects of the performance by each Sub-Specialist of its responsibilities in relation to the Specialist Works and no approval or other involvement by the Constructor in the selection or activities of any Sub-Specialist shall in any way relieve or affect that responsibility.
Replacement of Sub-Specialists	10.3	The Specialist shall not terminate any Sub-Specialist appointment without prior Consultation with the Constructor. If any Sub-Specialist appointment is so terminated, the Specialist shall replace that Sub-Specialist with an alternative Sub-Specialist of comparable expertise subject to prior approval by the Constructor.
Instructions to Sub-Specialists	10.4	Only the Specialist shall have authority to issue instructions to any Sub-Specialist.

SPC INTERNATIONAL   © ACA and Trowers & Hamlins 2007

11. VOLUME SUPPLY AGREEMENTS

Volume Supply Agreements

11.1 The Specialist shall utilise in relation to the Specialist Works any Volume Supply Agreements stated in the Specialist Agreement, subject to agreement with each relevant supplier, and shall assume responsibility for each such supplier as a Sub-Specialist.

12. SPECIALIST PRICE

Payment under Specialist Pre-Possession Agreement

12.1 In respect of activities under any Specialist Pre-Possession Agreement entered into pursuant to clause 13.3, the Constructor shall pay the Specialist those amounts stated in such Specialist Pre-Possession Agreement.

Profit, Central Office Overheads and Site Overheads

12.2 If so stated in the Specialist Payment Terms, the Specialist's Profit, Central Office Overheads and Site Overheads for the Specialist Works shall be fixed at the agreed amounts set out in the Specialist Payment Terms, subject only to such variations as the Constructor and the Specialist may agree, and shall form part of the Specialist Price.

Specialist Price

12.3 Prices for all aspects of the Specialist Works shall be as set out in the Specialist Payment Terms and as otherwise established in accordance with these Specialist Terms and shall together comprise the Specialist Price.

Specialist Budgets

12.4 If, in the Specialist Payment Terms, Specialist Budgets are stated for all or any part of the Specialist Works, then the relevant parts of the Specialist Price shall be established by the methods stated in the Specialist Payment Terms within the periods stated in the Specialist Timetable.

Discounts and third party benefits

12.5 No discounts or other benefits shall be payable by any party to the Specialist for prompt payment or otherwise unless stated in the Specialist Documents or otherwise agreed by the Constructor and the Specialist.

Risk contingencies

12.6 All and any proposed risk contingencies shall be notified by the Specialist to the Constructor, but shall only be incorporated in the Specialist Payment Terms and form part of the Specialist Price if and to the extent that any such risk contingency has been approved by the Constructor after the Constructor and the Specialist have first reviewed each relevant risk in accordance with clause 18.1 and have considered and agreed how the relevant risk should or could be eliminated, reduced, insured, shared or apportioned and the extent to which the risk contingency can be removed or reduced.

Cost savings and added value

12.7 The Constructor and the Specialist shall investigate the potential for cost savings against the Specialist Price and for added value in the implementation and Operation of the Specialist Works, and shall make recommendations to each other.

13. INCENTIVES

Appropriate incentives

13.1 The Constructor and the Specialist shall consider and seek to agree such incentives, additional to any described in the Specialist Documents, as may be appropriate to encourage them to maximise their efforts pursuant to the Specialist Contract for the benefit of the Specialist Works and the Project.

Shared savings and added value incentives

13.2 The Constructor and the Specialist shall implement, in the manner stated in the Specialist Payment Terms, any shared savings arrangements and added value incentives stated in the Specialist Agreement to be applicable to the Specialist.

Specialist Pre-Possession Agreement	13.3	The Constructor and the Specialist may agree that the Specialist shall undertake and be paid for Specialist Pre-Possession Activities forming part of the Specialist Works, in accordance with the terms of a Specialist Pre-Possession Agreement based on the form set out in Part 1 of Appendix 2, which shall be signed by the Constructor and the Specialist.
Specialist Pre-Possession Activities	13.4	In relation to all Specialist Pre-Possession Activities (except only as otherwise stated in the Specialist Pre-Possession Agreement):-

(i) Intellectual Property Rights, insurance obligations, risk, responsibility and ownership shall be governed by these Specialist Terms;

(ii) timing shall be governed by the Specialist Timetable;

(iii) the only payment shall be the amount or amounts stated in the Specialist Pre-Possession Agreement, payable under the procedures set out in these Specialist Terms;

(iv) problem solving and avoidance or resolution of disputes shall be governed by these Specialist Terms;

(v) the Specialist Pre-Possession Agreement shall not create any other obligations on either party;

(vi) all Specialist Pre-Possession Activities shall form part of the Specialist Works;

(vii) the Specialist shall cease all Specialist Pre-Possession Activities and vacate the Site if and when so requested by the Constructor.

Payment and Specialist KPIs	13.5	If and to the extent that the Specialist Documents link payment of the Specialist to achievement of the Date for Specialist Completion or any of the targets stated in the Specialist KPIs, then as soon as the level of such achievement is clearly demonstrable (and whether or not any adjustment appears in the Specialist's applications for payment), the Constructor shall determine the amount of any consequent additional or reduced payment in accordance with the Specialist Documents, and a corresponding adjustment shall be made in the next valuation or valuations of the Specialist Works pursuant to clause 20.3.

14. PRE-CONDITIONS

Pre-conditions to implementation of Specialist Works	14.1	Implementation of the Specialist Works shall commence subject to satisfaction of the pre-conditions for commencement of the Project on Site stated in the Partnering Contract and any further pre-conditions stated in the Specialist Agreement, either completely or to such lesser extent as the Constructor and the Specialist may agree.

15. IMPLEMENTATION OF SPECIALIST WORKS

Commencement Notices	15.1	Subject to satisfaction of the pre-conditions described in clause 14.1 and subject to these Specialist Terms, the Constructor shall issue any required Commencement Notices, based on the form set out in Part 2 of Appendix 2, in accordance with the Specialist Timetable.
Implementing Specialist Works	15.2	Commencing within the period or periods stated in the Specialist Timetable, whether from the date or dates of any required Commencement Notices or

SPC INTERNATIONAL © ACA and Trowers & Hamlins 2007

otherwise, the Specialist shall implement and complete the Specialist Works (or the relevant part specified in each Commencement Notice) in accordance with the Specialist Documents by the Date for Specialist Completion (subject to extension in accordance with these Specialist Terms), in consideration for which the Constructor shall pay to the Specialist the Specialist Price, subject only to such increases and decreases as are in accordance with these Specialist Terms.

Specialist on Site

15.3 Throughout the implementation of the Specialist Works until Specialist Completion in accordance with clause 21 (and also during the performance of any Specialist Pre-Possession Activities):-

(i) the Specialist's activities on Site shall be subject to such constraints as are referred to in the Specialist Documents;

(ii) the Specialist shall use reasonable skill and care, appropriate to its agreed role, expertise and responsibilities as stated in the Specialist Documents, to integrate the Specialist Works with the remainder of the Project and to integrate its activities with those of the Constructor and other Partnering Team members and Other Specialists;

(iii) the Constructor and other Partnering Team members shall have access at all reasonable times to all places where activities in connection with the Specialist Works are being carried out (which the Specialist shall in turn arrange with its Sub-Specialists), subject in all cases to reasonable prior notice and reasonable restrictions;

(iv) subject to any other security requirements stated in the Specialist Documents in respect of the Specialist Works, the Constructor shall be responsible for the security of the Project and the Site;

(v) subject to clauses 15.3(iv) and 18 and subject to any exceptions stated in the Specialist Agreement, the risk of loss or damage to the Specialist Works and all and any materials, goods and equipment intended for (or for use in connection with) the Specialist Works, whether on or off Site, shall remain with the Specialist;

(vi) the Specialist shall be liable for, and shall indemnify the Constructor against, any liability, damage, loss, expense, cost, claim or proceedings in respect of personal injury to or death of any person and in respect of loss of or damage to any property (except such property as is required to be insured pursuant to clause 19.1) arising out of or in connection with the implementation of the Specialist Works, whether arising on or off Site, provided that the Specialist's liability in respect of loss of or damage to any such property shall arise only insofar as this is due to any negligence, omission or default of the Specialist or any Sub-Specialist and provided also that the Specialist's liability to indemnify the Constructor under this clause 15.3(vi) shall reduce proportionately to the extent that the negligence, omission or default of the Constructor or any Partnering Team member (other than the Specialist) or any Other Specialist has contributed to the relevant injury, death, loss or damage.

Ownership of materials, goods and equipment

15.4 Ownership of all materials, goods and equipment intended for the Specialist Works shall pass to the Constructor when they are incorporated into the Project or when the Specialist receives payment for them pursuant to clause 20 or on such other date or event as is stated in the Specialist Agreement (whichever shall be the earlier). Where the value of any such materials, goods or equipment is included in a valuation pursuant to clause 20.3, the Specialist shall ensure that such materials, goods and equipment are not removed from the Site or from any other place where they are situated at the date of such valuation except for delivery to the Site, and that if situated off Site they are clearly marked as owned by the Client or the Constructor (as the Constructor shall instruct), and are stored separately and securely, and are insured for their full value against all customary risks in the names of the Client and/or the Constructor (as the Constructor shall instruct).

Partnering Contract support

15.5 In performing its obligations under the Specialist Contract within the scope of its agreed role, expertise and responsibilities as stated in the Specialist Documents, the Specialist shall:-

    (i) provide to the Constructor such information and assistance as shall be necessary to enable the Constructor to comply with its obligations under the Partnering Contract; and

    (ii) not by reason of any delay, default or failure place the Constructor in breach of the Partnering Contract.

16. QUALITY AND ENVIRONMENT

Quality of Specialist Works

16.1 The Constructor and the Specialist shall work together and individually, in accordance with the Specialist Documents, to achieve the quality of the Specialist Works described in the Specialist Documents and to seek in accordance with the Specialist KPIs to reduce defects in the Specialist Works, to increase their expected lifespan, to improve their Sustainability and to reduce the cost of their Operation.

Standards

16.2 In implementing the Specialist Works, the Specialist shall use and supply materials, goods and equipment of types and standards that are compliant with the Specialist Documents and otherwise appropriate to the Specialist Works.

Specialist Quality Management System

16.3 The Constructor and the Specialist shall implement a Specialist Quality Management System as set out in the Specialist Works Brief and Specialist Works Proposals.

Environmental risk and Hazardous Substances

16.4 The Specialist shall use reasonable skill and care appropriate to its agreed role, expertise and responsibilities as stated in the Specialist Documents:-

    (i) to implement the measures stated in the Specialist Documents to eliminate or render negligible the risk of harm to the Environment or migration of Hazardous Substances onto or from the Site; and

    (ii) not to transport to, generate, store, use, treat, dispose of or install at the Site any Hazardous Substance and not to cause any release of Hazardous Substances into or contamination of the Environment, except in accordance with the Environmental Laws applicable at the time of implementing the Specialist Works.

17. SPECIALIST CHANGE

Proposed Specialist Changes

17.1 The Specialist may propose a Specialist Change to the Constructor at any time if it is demonstrably in the best interests of the Specialist Works and/or the Project. Any such proposed Specialist Change shall be considered by the Constructor and, if approved by the Constructor, shall then be notified by the Constructor to the Specialist in accordance with clause 17.2.

Specialist Changes	17.2	The Constructor may propose a Specialist Change at any time by notification to the Specialist and, upon notification of a proposed Specialist Change (or following compliance with clause 5.2 or clause 8.8 if applicable) the Specialist shall within nine (9) Working Days (or such other period as may be agreed) submit to the Constructor a Specialist Change Submission comprising its proposals as to the effect of the proposed Specialist Change on the Specialist Price, calculated on the basis of the Specialist Payment Terms and/or as to its effect on the progress of the Specialist Works and the Date for Specialist Completion, calculated on the basis of the Specialist Timetable.

Specialist Change Submission	17.3	The Constructor shall consider any Specialist Change Submission submitted pursuant to clause 17.2 and shall seek to agree it with the Specialist (with or without modification). By notice within ten (10) Working Days from the date of a Specialist Change Submission (or such other period as may be agreed), the Constructor shall:-

    (i)   instruct the Specialist to proceed with the Specialist Change (whether or not reserving any aspect of the Specialist Change Submission for later agreement or suggested modification); or

    (ii)   withdraw the proposed Specialist Change.

Evaluation of Specialist Change if not agreed	17.4	If the Constructor instructs the Specialist to proceed with a Specialist Change pursuant to clause 17.3, but the Constructor and the Specialist have not agreed within a further fifteen (15) Working Days from the date of such instruction any time and/or cost proposals in the Specialist Change Submission, then the Constructor shall ascertain the time and cost effects of such Specialist Change on a fair and reasonable basis utilising wherever possible relevant periods of time in the Specialist Timetable and prices for similar work in the Specialist Payment Terms, and within a further twenty (20) Working Days from expiry of the period for agreement shall notify the Specialist accordingly. If the Specialist disputes any consequent adjustment to the Specialist Price or the Date for Specialist Completion, it shall notify such dispute under clause 27.2 (or under clause 27.1 of the Partnering Terms if the Specialist is a Partnering Team member) within fifteen (15) Working Days from the date of the Constructor's notice and, in the absence of such notification of dispute or pending its resolution, the adjustment to the Specialist Price and/or the Date for Specialist Completion set out in the Constructor's notice shall prevail.

Urgent Specialist Change	17.5	If the Constructor considers a proposed Specialist Change to be sufficiently urgent, the Constructor may instruct the Specialist to proceed with that Specialist Change by reference to this clause 17.5, in advance of a Specialist Change Submission, which shall then be submitted in accordance with clause 17.2 and considered and evaluated in accordance with clause 17.4.

Minimum adverse effects	17.6	In all cases a Specialist Change Submission shall minimise, by means of effective Value Management and otherwise, any adverse effect on the Specialist Price and the Date for Specialist Completion, and shall reflect the spirit and content of the Specialist Documents, and the Constructor shall assist in achieving these objectives within its agreed role, expertise and responsibilities.

Effect of Specialist Change	17.7	Any Specialist Change and its effect on the Specialist Price and/or the Date for Specialist Completion, when agreed or established in accordance with this clause 17, shall be binding on the Constructor and the Specialist.

18. RISK MANAGEMENT

Risk
Management

18.1 The Constructor and the Specialist recognise the risks involved in the design, supply and construction of the Specialist Works, and the costs associated with those risks, and shall work together and individually, through Risk Management exercises in accordance with the Specialist Documents, to analyse and manage risks in the most effective ways including:-

(i) identifying risks and their likely costs;

(ii) eliminating or reducing risks and their costs;

(iii) insuring risks wherever affordable and appropriate;

(iv) sharing or apportioning risks according to which of the Constructor or the Specialist is most able to manage such risks.

Specialist risk

18.2 Throughout the implementation of the Specialist Works until the Specialist Completion Date, the Specialist shall be responsible for managing all risks associated with the Specialist Works, except as otherwise stated in these Specialist Terms and in any risk sharing arrangements set out in the Specialist Agreement.

Extensions of
time

18.3 The Specialist shall use its best endeavours at all times to minimise any delay or increased cost in the Specialist Works. Subject to the Specialist's compliance with the procedures set out in clause 18.4, the Specialist shall be entitled to be granted an appropriate extension of the Date for Specialist Completion if and to the extent that, despite the Specialist's best endeavours, any of the following adversely affect the Date for Specialist Completion:-

(i) a delay caused by a default or failure of the Constructor (except to the extent caused or contributed to by the Specialist or any Sub-Specialist or any other party for whom the Specialist is responsible) beyond any agreed time limit stated in these Specialist Terms or the Specialist Timetable, provided that the Specialist has given Early Warning to the Constructor in accordance with clause 3.3 not less than six (6) Working Days before expiry of the agreed time limit;

(ii) discovery of an Antiquity (and these shall belong to the Client and shall be handed over to the Constructor) not indicated in or reasonably apparent from an inspection of the Site or the results of any Site surveys and investigations carried out by or provided to the Specialist prior to the date of the Commencement Agreement under the Partnering Contract;

(iii) delay in receipt of any of the third party consents listed in the Specialist Agreement, provided that the Specialist has taken all proper and timely steps to avoid or reduce such delay;

(iv) a change in any law or regulation of the country in which the Site is located after the date of the Commencement Agreement under the Partnering Contract and not reasonably foreseeable by the Specialist;

(v) weather conditions which the meteorological office records for the area nearest to the Site indicate are exceptionally adverse for the time of year;

SPC INTERNATIONAL   © ACA and Trowers & Hamlins 2007

(vi)   delay by a local authority or statutory body or utility in carrying out work pursuant to its statutory obligations in relation to the Specialist Works, provided that the Specialist has supplied all necessary information, placed all necessary orders and otherwise performed its obligations under the Specialist Contract in respect of such work as soon as reasonably practicable and so as to not to delay or disrupt the local authority or statutory body or utility in relation to such work;

(vii)   opening up for inspection or testing of any part of the Specialist Works if such inspection or testing does not reveal anything not in accordance with the Specialist Documents, except where such opening up for inspection or testing was reasonable in view of similar non-compliance with the Specialist Documents having been discovered in another part of the Specialist Works;

(viii)   loss or damage occasioned by any one or more of the matters required to be insured pursuant to clause 19.1, where such insurance is required to be taken out by the Specialist;

(ix)   strike or other industrial action by employees of any party other than the Specialist or any Partnering Team member;

(x)   exercise, after the Date of Possession under the Partnering Contract, by the government of the country in which the Site is located of any statutory power directly affecting the implementation of the Specialist Works by restricting labour, materials, goods or equipment required for the Specialist Works;

(xi)   subject to clauses 6.3 and 15.3(i), failure by the Client or the Constructor to allow access to or possession of all or any part of the Site, to the extent that such access and possession are within the Client's or the Constructor's control;

(xii)   suspension of the Specialist Works in accordance with clause 26.8 or clause 26.9;

(xiii)   use or threat of terrorism affecting or reasonably likely to affect the Specialist Works or any individuals engaged on the Specialist Works, or causing restricted access to or any restricted activities on Site;

(xiv)   breach of the Specialist Contract by the Constructor of which the Specialist has given Early Warning;

(xv)   subject to clause 15.3(ii), delay, damage or obstruction by the Constructor or any other Partnering Team member or any Other Specialist (except to the extent caused or contributed to by the Specialist or any Sub-Specialist or any other party for whom the Specialist is responsible) provided that the Specialist has taken all reasonable precautions to avoid or reduce such delay, damage or obstruction;

(xvi)   any other event stated by reference to this clause 18.3(xvi) in the Specialist Agreement.

Notification of events

18.4   The Specialist shall:-

    (i)   notify the Constructor as soon as it becomes aware of any of the events described in clause 18.3, together with appropriate evidence and detailed proposals consistent with the Specialist Documents for overcoming such events and minimising their adverse effects on the cost, time for completion and quality of the Specialist Works; and

    (ii)   implement such proposals unless the Constructor instructs otherwise within four (4) Working Days from the date of such notification; and

    (iii)   provide such reasonable additional information as the Constructor may request

and the Constructor shall respond within twenty five (25) Working Days from the date of notification in accordance with clauses 18.4(i) and 18.4(iii) and ascertain any fair and reasonable extension of time in accordance with clause 18.3, taking into account the Specialist Timetable, and in its response shall ascertain any fair and reasonable additional Site Overheads in accordance with clause 18.5 and any other fair and reasonable increase in the Specialist Price in accordance with clause 18.6, taking into account the Specialist Payment Terms. If the Specialist disputes any such extension of time or increase in the Specialist Price, it shall notify such dispute under clause 27.2 (or under clause 27.1 of the Partnering Terms if the Specialist is a Partnering Team member) within fifteen (15) Working Days from the date of the Constructor's response. In the absence of such notice of dispute or pending resolution of any such dispute, the Specialist shall be entitled to any extension of time and any increase in the Specialist Price stated in the Constructor's response.

Time-based Site Overheads

18.5   Where an event described in clause 18.3, other than an event described in any of clauses 18.3(iii), 18.3(v), 18.3(vi), 18.3(viii), 18.3(ix) and 18.3(x) (subject to any agreed adjustment in the Specialist Agreement), gives rise to an extension of the Date for Specialist Completion then, in respect of those Site Overheads agreed to be time-based in the Specialist Payment Terms, proportionate appropriate additional Site Overheads shall be added to the Specialist Price.

Unavoidable work or expenditure

18.6   Where an event described in clause 18.3, other than an event described in any of clauses 18.3(iii), 18.3(v), 18.3(vi), 18.3(viii), 18.3(ix) and 18.3(x) (subject to any agreed adjustment in the Specialist Agreement), and whether or not such event gives rise to an extension of the Date for Specialist Completion, properly requires unavoidable additional work or expenditure, then such work or expenditure (if not within the scope of matters covered by Central Office Overheads or Site Overheads) shall be included in the Specialist's proposals pursuant to clause 18.4, calculated wherever possible on the basis of the Specialist Payment Terms and subject to the following conditions:-

    (i)   the Specialist shall minimise the amount of any such additional work or expenditure and its cost and duration;

    (ii)   the cost of any such additional work or expenditure shall be calculated and presented on an Open-book basis and shall not include any additional Profit or Central Office Overheads or any loss of profit on other projects;

    (iii)   the Specialist shall not be entitled to claim any additional payment of any kind, other than those payments described in clause 18.5 and this clause 18.6, by reason of any event described in clause 18.3.

SPC INTERNATIONAL   © ACA and Trowers & Hamlins 2007

Site Environment	18.7	Subject to clause 18.3(ii) and any other exceptions and clarifications stated in the Specialist Agreement, the Specialist shall be deemed to have satisfied itself as to the state and condition of the Environment comprising the Site insofar as it affects implementation of the Specialist Works.
Delay or disruption by Sub-Specialists	18.8	Any delay or disruption caused by any Sub-Specialist (or by its termination and replacement) shall be at the risk of the Specialist and shall not give rise to any extension of the Date for Specialist Completion or any increase in the Specialist Price or entitle the Specialist to claim additional payment of any kind.

19. INSURANCE AND SECURITY

Insurance of Specialist Works, Project and Site	19.1	Insurance of the Specialist Works, the Project and the Site and any structures on it shall be taken out by the party or parties named in the Specialist Agreement, in the joint names of the parties and with waivers of subrogation as each stated in the Specialist Agreement, for the risks stated in Section 1 of Part 1 of Appendix 3 and any additional or adjusted risks stated in the Specialist Agreement and, if so stated in the Specialist Agreement, for third party property damage cover in the amount stated in the Specialist Agreement and for the risks stated in Section 2 of Part 1 of Appendix 3.
Repair and restoration	19.2	Upon the occurrence of any event giving rise to a claim under any insurance policy described in clause 19.1, and subject to clauses 26.8 and 26.9, the Specialist in accordance with the Constructor's instructions shall repair and restore the Specialist Works, replace any work, materials, goods and equipment damaged or destroyed, remove all debris from the Site and continue with the implementation and completion of the Specialist Works. If and to the extent that such insurance is to be taken out by the Specialist, then no additional payment shall be due as a result, whereas if and to the extent that such insurance is to be taken out by any other party, then such repair, restoration, replacement and removal shall be treated as a Specialist Change in accordance with clause 17.
Third party insurance	19.3	Third party liability insurance shall be taken out by the Specialist and maintained throughout the period that the Specialist participates in the Project in the amount stated in the Specialist Agreement and for the risks stated in Part 2 of Appendix 3.
Professional indemnity/ product liability insurance	19.4	Professional indemnity insurance and/or product liability insurance shall be taken out by the Specialist for the amounts (if any) stated in the Specialist Agreement, for the risks stated in Part 3 of Appendix 3, and shall be maintained throughout the limitation period referred to in clause 27.7, unless such cover is no longer generally available in the market-place on reasonable terms and at reasonable premiums.
Environmental Risk Insurance	19.5	If so stated in the Partnering Contract, Environmental Risk Insurance shall be taken out and maintained by the party stated in the Partnering Contract, in the amounts and for the risks and period stated in the Partnering Contract.
Latent Defects Insurance	19.6	If so stated in the Partnering Contract, Latent Defects Insurance shall be taken out by the party stated in the Partnering Contract, in the amount and for the risks and period stated in the Partnering Contract. The Specialist shall comply with all the reasonable requirements of the Latent Defects Insurance provider as to inspection and provision of information.
Whole Project Insurance	19.7	If so stated in the Partnering Contract, the Project shall be covered by the Whole Project Insurance described in the Partnering Contract.

Insurance obligations	19.8	In relation to all insurances described in this clause 19, the Constructor and the Specialist shall fulfil the obligations set out in Part 4 of Appendix 3.
Other forms of security	19.9	If so stated in the Specialist Works Brief, the Specialist shall provide to the Constructor:-

(i)   not later than fifteen (15) Working Days prior to the Specialist's first application for payment, an advance payment guarantee and/or a performance bond in the forms annexed to the Specialist Agreement and in the amounts stated in the Specialist Agreement, executed by a bank or insurance company acceptable to the Constructor, and/or a parent company guarantee in the form annexed to the Specialist Agreement, executed by the Specialist's ultimate holding company; and/or

(ii)   on the date stated in the Specialist Works Brief, a retention bond in the form annexed to the Specialist Agreement and in the amount stated in the Specialist Agreement, executed by a bank or insurance company acceptable to the Constructor.

20.   PAYMENT

Payment obligations	20.1	The Constructor shall be responsible for payment to the Specialist of all agreed amounts under any Specialist Pre-Possession Agreement and comprising the Specialist Price in each case subject to and adjusted in accordance with these Specialist Terms.
Payment applications	20.2	Subject to any agreed payment milestones, activity schedules or cashflows and any other payment arrangements set out in the Specialist Payment Terms, applications for payment of amounts due to the Specialist shall be submitted by the Specialist to the Constructor at the intervals stated in the Specialist Payment Terms or (if no intervals are stated) at intervals of one calendar month, the first application being made not later than the relevant interval after the date stated in the Specialist Agreement or (if no date is stated) the relevant interval after the date of commencement of the Specialist Works in accordance with the Specialist Contract. Each application for payment shall be accompanied by such details as are stated in the Specialist Works Brief and such further information as the Constructor may reasonably require.
Valuations and payments to Specialist	20.3	Subject to any revised period stated in the Specialist Agreement, within ten (10) Working Days from receipt of each application for payment made by the Specialist in accordance with clause 20.2 and when otherwise required by these Specialist Terms, the Constructor shall issue to the Specialist a valuation calculated in accordance with clause 20.4, specifying the amount of the payment proposed to be made, to what that amount relates and the basis on which that amount is calculated. The date of such valuation shall be the due date for payment to the Specialist. Subject to any revised period stated in the Specialist Agreement, the Constructor shall pay to the Specialist the amount stated as due in each such valuation within fifteen (15) Working Days from the date of issue of such valuation or ten (10) Working Days from the date of receipt by the Constructor of any required invoice in the same amount from the Specialist, whichever shall be the later, and the later of such dates shall be the final date for payment.
Content of Specialist valuations	20.4	The amount payable under each application for payment by the Specialist shall be calculated in accordance with the Specialist Payment Terms to establish the value

of any Specialist Pre-Possession Activities properly performed or the value of that part of the Specialist Works properly progressed, including the value of any unfixed materials, goods and equipment on and off Site intended for the Specialist Works (subject to clause 15.4 and if and to the extent provided in the Specialist Payment Terms), less the total of all amounts previously paid, and adjusted to reflect any shared savings pursuant to clause 13.2 and any linkage between payment and achievement of Specialist KPI targets pursuant to clause 13.5.

Withholding or deduction	20.5	Not later than two (2) Working Days before the final date for payment of any amount due, the Constructor may give notice to the Specialist specifying any amount proposed to be withheld or deducted from the amount otherwise due together with the ground or grounds for such withholding or deduction and the amount attributable to each such ground.
Adjustment of valuations	20.6	None of the issue by the Constructor of any valuation or by the Specialist of an invoice or the payment of any amount by the Constructor shall in any way affect the right of the Constructor or the Specialist to contend that any Specialist Pre-Possession Activities or the Specialist Works have not been properly valued and that any amount has been improperly paid or withheld and, in calculating any valuation, the Constructor shall be entitled to reconsider and, if necessary, adjust any assessment made in arriving at any previous valuation.
Valuations not approval	20.7	None of the issue by the Constructor of any valuation or by the Specialist of an invoice or the payment of any amount by the Constructor shall constitute or imply or be evidence of the Constructor's approval or acceptance of any part of any Specialist Pre-Possession Activities or the Specialist Works or shall in any way affect the responsibilities of the Specialist under the Specialist Contract.
Interest on late payment	20.8	Any delay in a due payment beyond the final date stated in clause 20.3 shall entitle the Specialist to be paid interest at the percentage specified in the Specialist Agreement.
Fluctuation	20.9	The Specialist Price shall be subject only to such fluctuation provisions, if any, as are set out in the Specialist Payment Terms.
Payment of Sub-Specialists	20.10	The Specialist shall pay all Sub-Specialists the amounts to which they are entitled (with provision for interest on late payment equivalent to clause 20.8), shall maintain full records of all amounts payable and paid and shall make these records available to the Constructor on request.
Payment on Specialist Completion	20.11	Within twenty five (25) Working Days following Specialist Completion (or any other period stated in the Specialist Agreement), the Constructor shall prepare and issue to the Specialist an account confirming the balance of the Specialist Price due as between the Constructor and the Specialist, subject only to any outstanding entitlements and claims by the Constructor or the Specialist notified to the other party prior to that date, and the Constructor and the Specialist shall seek to agree the amount of that balance, taking into account any adjustment provided for in these Specialist Terms and subject to deduction of any amount stated as a Specialist Retention in the Specialist Payment Terms. Within twenty five (25) Working Days from the date of issue of that account, the Constructor shall issue a valuation in accordance with clause 20.3 in the agreed amount, or if agreement is not reached then, subject to clause 20.6, in such amount as is fair and reasonable. The Constructor shall pay in accordance with clause 20.3 the amount stated as due in such valuation.

Specialist Final Account	20.12	Within twenty (20) Working Days from the date or event stated in the Specialist Agreement, the Constructor shall prepare and issue to the Specialist a Specialist Final Account in respect of the Specialist Works for agreement between the Constructor and the Specialist. The Specialist Final Account, when agreed, shall be conclusive evidence as to the balance of the Specialist Price due as between the Constructor and the Specialist and, upon agreement, the Constructor shall issue a Specialist Final Account valuation. The Constructor shall pay in accordance with clause 20.3 the amount stated as due in such valuation, and clause 20.6 shall not apply to such valuation.
Non-agreement of Specialist Final Account	20.13	If agreement of the Specialist Final Account is not reached within forty (40) Working Days from the date of its issue in accordance with clause 20.12, either the Constructor or the Specialist may implement the procedure described in clause 27 if appropriate.

21. SPECIALIST COMPLETION AND SUPPORT

Notice of Specialist Completion	21.1	When the Specialist considers that the Specialist Works are about to achieve Specialist Completion, it shall give the Constructor not less than seven (7) Working Days notice (or such other period of notice as may be stated in the Specialist Works Brief), requesting the Constructor to attend, inspect and test as provided for in the Specialist Works Brief. The Specialist shall not request such attendance, inspection or testing at any time excluded in the Specialist Works Brief, or without handing over such documents and completing such pre-conditions and procedures as are specified in the Specialist Works Brief.
Inspection and testing	21.2	The Constructor and other appropriate Partnering Team members shall attend, inspect and test as requested in accordance with clause 21.1 and, within four (4) Working Days following completion of such attendance, inspection and testing, the Constructor shall issue a notice to the Specialist either:-

(i)   confirming that the Specialist Works have achieved Specialist Completion; or

(ii)   stating where any aspect of the Specialist Works is not in accordance with the Specialist Documents, in which case the Specialist shall rectify such non-compliance and again present the Specialist Works in accordance with clause 21.1.

Part Specilaist Completion	21.3	The Constructor and the Specialist may agree early attendance, inspection and testing for Specialist Completion of any part of the Specialist Works and, following a procedure equivalent to that described in clauses 21.1 and 21.2 or such other procedure as may be agreed by the Constructor and the Specialist, the defects rectification arrangements described in clause 21.4 shall apply to that part of the Specialist Works.
Rectification of defects	21.4	Following confirmation of Specialist Completion in accordance with clause 21.2(i) the Specialist shall attend the Site whenever notified by the Constructor of any defects, excessive shrinkages or other faults in the Specialist Works which may appear before Specialist Completion or within the Specialist Defects Liability Period stated in the Specialist Agreement and which are due to materials, goods, equipment or workmanship not in accordance with the Specialist Documents. Such defects, excessive shrinkages or other faults shall be rectified by the Specialist at no cost to the Contstructor within the periods stated in the Specialist Agreement unless the Constructor shall otherwise instruct.

SPC INTERNATIONAL © ACA and Trowers & Hamlins 2007

Confirmation of rectification of defects	21.5	The Constructor shall issue a notice to the Specialist confirming the date when the Specialist's obligations under clause 21.4 have been satisfied and, with effect from the date of such notice, such obligations shall be treated as having been satisfied.
Operation of completed Specialist Works	21.6	The Specialist may submit to the Constructor proposals for the Operation of the completed Specialist Works, which the Constructor shall consider and may notify to the Client.

22. DUTY OF CARE AND WARRANTIES

Skill and care	22.1	In all their activities relating to the implementation of the Specialist Works and all incidental activities governed by the Specialist Documents, the Constructor and the Specialist shall use reasonable skill and care appropriate to their respective roles, expertise and responsibilities as stated in the Specialist Documents, and shall owe each other such duty of care in respect of all their agreed obligations under the Specialist Contract, with only such amendments and restrictions as are stated in the Specialist Agreement.
Direct Agreements	22.2	The Specialist shall provide for the benefit of each of the parties stated in the Specialist Agreement direct agreements in the specified forms annexed to the Specialist Agreement if and when so requested by the Constructor.
Sub-Specialist warranties	22.3	The Specialist shall obtain and submit to the Constructor such direct warranties in favour of the Client in respect of individual parts of the Specialist Works as are described in the Specialist Works Brief or the Specialist Works Proposals and any additional direct warranties offered by or available from particular Sub-Specialists.
Third party rights	22.4	Except as otherwise stated in the Specialist Agreement, and notwithstanding any other provision of the Specialist Terms, and without prejudice to any direct agreement entered into pursuant to clause 22.2, nothing in the Specialist Contract confers or purports to confer any benefit or right to enforce any of its terms on any person who is not a party to it.

23. SPECIALIST KPIS AND CONTINUOUS IMPROVEMENT

Specialist KPIs	23.1	The performance of the Constructor and the Specialist shall be kept under regular mutual review by reference to the Specialist KPIs. The Constructor and the Specialist shall use reasonable skill and care, within the scope of their agreed roles, expertise and responsibilities and in accordance with the Specialist Documents, to achieve their respective targets as set out in the Specialist KPIs.
Measurable continuous improvement	23.2	Each of the Constructor and the Specialist shall provide to the other such information as may be reasonably necessary to demonstrate progress against its Specialist KPIs.
Post-Specialist Completion review	23.3	The Constructor and the Specialist shall attend a meeting convened by the Constructor in accordance with clause 3.4 after Specialist Completion, to review the completed Specialist Works and the performance of the Constructor and the Specialist against the Specialist KPIs, and to consider the scope for further improvement on future projects.

24. JOINT INITIATIVES AND STRATEGIC ALLIANCING

Joint
initiatives

24.1 The Constructor and the Specialist shall pursue together such joint initiatives for the benefit of Specialist Works and the Project as they may agree to be appropriate and consistent with the Specialist Contract.

Strategic
alliancing

24.2 The Constructor and the Specialist recognise the benefits of developing a strategic alliancing relationship for the implementation of further projects and agree to develop such a relationship, subject to their respective performance against the Specialist KPIs and subject to agreement of specific terms between them consistent with current applicable laws and regulations in force in the country referred to in clause 27.6.

25. GENERAL

Exclusion of
partnership

25.1 Nothing in the Specialist Documents shall create, or be construed as creating, a partnership between the Constructor and the Specialist and neither shall conduct itself in such a way as to create an impression that such a partnership exists.

Assignment
and
sub-contracting

25.2 The Specialist Contract is personal to the Constructor and the Specialist and none of the rights or obligations of either party may be assigned or sub-contracted without the prior consent of the other except as stated in the Specialist Agreement or in accordance with these Specialist Terms.

Whole
Specialist
Contract

25.3 The Specialist Documents (and, if the Specialist is a Partnering Team member, the Partnering Contract) shall together represent the entire understanding between the Constructor and the Specialist in relation to the Specialist Works. No amendment to the Specialist Documents shall be valid or binding unless made in writing and signed by the Constructor and the Specialist, or otherwise made in accordance with these Specialist Terms.

Laws and
regulations

25.4 The Constructor and the Specialist shall comply with all laws and regulations currently in force in the country stated in the Specialist Agreement and in the country in which the Site is located, and with the terms of all statutory and other legally binding requirements relating to implementation of the Specialist Works.

Confidentiality

25.5 The Constructor and the Specialist shall not reveal to any third party (except as expressly agreed or as obliged by law) any information exchanged between them, if and to the extent that it is stated or known by them to be confidential, and shall use such information only for the purposes of the Project.

26. TERMINATION

Termination for
unforeseeable
reasons

26.1 The Constructor may terminate the appointment of the Specialist under the Specialist Contract, due to non-achievement of any of the pre-conditions set out in or by reference to clause 14.1, by not less than ten (10) Working Days prior notice stating the reason. If the appointments of all Partnering Team members are terminated under clause 26.1 of the Partnering Terms, then the appointment of the Specialist under the Specialist Contract shall automatically terminate on the same date and the Constructor shall notify the Specialist of the date of and reason for such termination within five (5) Working Days following receipt by the Constructor of notice under clause 26.1 of the Partnering Terms. Upon either such termination the Specialist shall submit an application for payment in accordance with clause 20.2, and the Constructor shall issue a valuation pursuant to clause 20.3, in respect of the amount due to the Specialist and relating to any expressly approved activities

SPC INTERNATIONAL © ACA and Trowers & Hamlins 2007

carried out prior to the effective date of termination. The Constructor shall pay in accordance with clause 20 the amount stated in such valuation but shall not be liable to pay any other amount to the Specialist. No termination may be effected under this clause 26.1 after the date of any Commencement Notice in relation to that part of the Specialist Works referred to in such Commencement Notice.

Bankruptcy or insolvency

26.2   In the event that under the law of the country where either the Constructor or the Specialist or the Site as located the Constructor or the Specialist shall become bankrupt, or make a composition or arrangement with its creditors, or make a proposal in respect of its company for a voluntary arrangement for a composition of debts or a scheme of arrangement to be approved, or have any steps taken in or out of court in respect of its company for the appointment of an administrator, or have a winding up order made, or (except for the purposes of amalgamation or reconstruction) have a resolution for voluntary winding up passed, or have a provisional liquidator, receiver or manager of its business or undertaking duly appointed, or have an administrative receiver appointed, or have possession taken by or on behalf of the holders of any debenture secured by a floating charge, the appointment of the Specialist under the Specialist Contract shall automatically terminate with immediate effect.

Termination for Specialist breach

26.3   In the event that the Specialist:-

(i)   without entitlement under these Specialist Terms, ceases or suspends all or a significant part of the implementation of the Specialist Works or does not commence and continue to fulfil its responsibilities under the Specialist Contract in accordance with the Specialist Timetable; or

(ii)   fails to comply with an instruction of the Constructor that is in accordance with the Specialist Documents, following notice from the Constructor in accordance with clause 5.4; or

(iii)   breaches clause 25.2; or

(iv)   breaches clause 25.4 so as to adversely affect the interests of the Specialist Works or the Project or any Partnering Team member

and if the Specialist shall not remedy such breach within ten (10) Working Days from the date of notice from the Constructor specifying the breach, then (subject to prior compliance by the Constructor with any relevant obligations under clause 26.3 of the Partnering Terms) the Constructor may terminate the appointment of the Specialist under the Specialist Contract by further notice to the Specialist with immediate effect.

Arrangements following termination for Specialist bankruptcy, insolvency or breach

26.4   Following termination of the appointment of the Specialist under clause 26.2 (by reason of the Specialist suffering an event described in that clause) or under clause 26.3:-

(i)   the Constructor may complete the Specialist Works using others and shall not be bound to make any further payment to the Specialist until the full and final cost of completion of the Specialist Works by others has been ascertained, at which time if such amount, when added to the amounts already paid to the Specialist in respect of the Specialist Works prior to the date of termination, exceeds the Specialist Price, then the difference shall be payable to the Constructor by the Specialist;

(ii) the Constructor and other Partnering Team members (other than the Specialist) and Other Specialists may use all temporary buildings, plant, tools, materials, goods and equipment intended for (or for use in connection with) the Specialist Works and delivered to the Site and after such use or at any other time the Constructor may instruct the Specialist to remove any such items and, if any such items are not removed by the Specialist when instructed, the Constructor may (but without being responsible for any loss or damage) remove and sell any such items holding the proceeds less all costs incurred to the credit of the Specialist;

(iii) the Specialist shall, if so required by the Constructor at any time, assign to the Constructor without payment the benefit of any agreement for the supply of materials or goods or equipment and/or for the execution of any works or services for the purposes of the Specialist Works to the extent that the same is assignable and to the extent permitted by law; and

(iv) the Constructor may pay any Sub-Specialist for any materials or goods or equipment delivered to the Site or any works or services executed for the purposes of the Specialist Works, in any such case before termination of the Specialist's appointment and insofar as their price has not already been paid by the Specialist and to the extent permitted by law.

Termination for Constructor breach

26.5 In the event that the Constructor:-

(i) without entitlement, under these Specialist Terms or the Partnering Contract, ceases or suspends all or a significant part of the Project or does not commence and continue implementation of the Project so that the reasonable progress of the Specialist Works cannot be maintained in accordance with the Specialist Timetable; or

(ii) fails to value or make any payment due to the Specialist in accordance with the Specialist Documents by the final date for payment under clause 20.3; or

(iii) breaches clause 25.2; or

(iv) breaches clause 25.4 so as to adversely affect the interests of the Specialist Works or the Specialist

and if the Constructor shall not remedy such breach within ten (10) Working Days from the date of notice from the Specialist specifying the breach, then (subject to prior compliance by the Specialist with any relevant obligations under clause 26.11 of the Partnering Terms) the Specialist may terminate its own appointment under the Specialist Contract by further notice to the Constructor with immediate effect.

Termination under Partnering Contract

26.6 If the appointment of the Constructor under the Partnering Contract is terminated under clause 26.2 of the Partnering Terms (by reason of the Client suffering an event described in that clause) or under clause 26.4 of the Partnering Terms (for any reason not attributable to the Specialist) or clause 26.5 of the Partnering

SPC INTERNATIONAL © ACA and Trowers & Hamlins 2007

Terms, then the appointment of the Specialist under the Specialist Contract shall automatically terminate on the same date and the Constructor shall give immediate notice of this to the Specialist.

Arrangements following termination for Constructor bankruptcy, insolvency, breach or termination under Partnering Contract

26.7   Within fifteen (15) Working Days from the date of termination of the appointment of the Specialist under clause 26.2 (by reason of the Constructor suffering an event described in that clause) or under clause 26.5 or under clause 26.6, the Specialist shall submit an application for payment in accordance with clause 20.2, and the Constructor shall issue a valuation pursuant to clause 20.3 in respect of the total amount properly due to the Specialist up to the date of termination (including the value of all materials, goods and equipment in respect of which the Specialist has made commitment in accordance with the Specialist Timetable prior to the date of termination and has transferred unencumbered ownership to the Constructor and the Specialist's reasonable costs under clause 26.11) and the Constructor shall pay such amount in accordance with clause 20 subject (only in the case of termination under clause 26.6 by reason of the Client suffering an event described in clause 26.2 of the Partnering Terms) to any arrangements in the Specialist Payment Terms.

Suspension or abandonment

26.8   If it becomes impossible to proceed with or complete the Specialist Works, by reason of loss or damage to the Specialist Works caused by any risk required to be insured under clause 19.1, or any civil commotion, or any act or omission of the government of the country in which the Site is located or any local authority or statutory body or utility, or hostilities involving the country in which the Site is located, or terrorist activity, despite the Constructor and the Specialist having used their best endeavours to avoid or overcome the consequences of any such event, then the Constructor or the Specialist (whichever shall first become aware of such occurrence) shall give immediate notice to the other and they shall together consider the problem and any possible solutions. Unless the Constructor and the Specialist agree such a solution within twenty (20) Working Days from the date of the first notice of such occurrence, the Constructor by notice to the Specialist with immediate effect shall suspend implementation of the Specialist Works and/or abandon the Specialist Works.

Suspension or abandonment under Partnering Contract

26.9   If performance of the Constructor's obligations under the Partnering Contract is suspended in accordance with clause 20.17 of the Partnering Terms or if the Project is suspended or abandoned in accordance with clause 26.6 of the Partnering Terms, the Constructor shall immediately give notice to the Specialist suspending (or, if the Project is abandoned, abandoning) implementation of the Specialist Works with immediate effect and stating the reason.

Consequences of suspension or abandonment

26.10   With effect from three (3) calendar months following Constructor notice of suspension under clause 26.8 or with immediate effect following Constructor notice of abandonment under clauses 26.8 or 26.9, or with immediate effect following abandonment of the Project in accordance with clause 26.7 of the Partnering Terms (which the Constructor shall immediately notify to the Specialist), the appointment of the Specialist under the Specialist Contract shall automatically terminate unless the Constructor and the Specialist agree otherwise, and the Specialist shall submit an application for payment in accordance with clause 20.2, and the Constructor shall issue a valuation pursuant to clause 20.3, in respect of the total amount properly due to the Specialist up to the date of suspension or abandonment (including the value of all materials, goods and equipment in respect of which the Specialist has made commitment in accordance with the Specialist Timetable prior to the date of suspension or abandonment and has transferred unencumbered ownership to the Constructor, and the Specialist's reasonable costs under clause 26.11) and the Constructor shall pay such amount in accordance with clause 20.

Protection of Specialist Works	26.11	Immediately following termination of the Specialist's appointment pursuant to any of clauses 26.2, 26.3, 26.5 or 26.6 or suspension or abandonment pursuant to either of clauses 26.8 or 26.9, the Specialist shall properly protect and secure the Specialist Works and (except, in the event of suspension, pending operation of clause 26.10) deliver to the Constructor possession of the Specialist Works.
Accrued rights and obligations	26.12	Termination of the appointment of the Specialist shall not affect the mutual rights and obligations of the Constructor and the Specialist accrued at the date of termination and their ongoing obligations under clauses 9, 19.4 and 25.5 and under this clause 26.

27. PROBLEM SOLVING AND DISPUTE AVOIDANCE OR RESOLUTION

Partnering Team Specialist difference or dispute	27.1	If the Specialist is a Partnering Team member, then any difference or dispute arising under or out of or in connection with the Specialist Contract or the Specialist Works (a "Specialist difference or dispute") shall be resolved in accordance with the procedures described in the Partnering Contract as if clauses 27.1, 27.2, 27.3, 27.4 and 27.5 and Appendix 5 of the Partnering Terms also formed part of the Specialist Contract and as if the references to a difference or dispute in those clauses also referred to a Specialist difference or dispute and as if clauses 27.2, 27.3, 27.4 and 27.5 were deleted from the Specialist Terms.
Notice of Specialist difference or dispute	27.2	As soon as it is aware of any Specialist difference or dispute, the Constructor or the Specialist shall give notice to the other.
Specialist Problem-Solving Hierarchy	27.3	Upon receipt of a notice in accordance with clause 27.2 the Constructor and the Specialist shall apply the Specialist Problem-Solving Hierarchy set out in the Specialist Agreement and shall use reasonable skill and care to ensure that their employees named in the Specialist Problem-Solving Hierarchy shall express their views and propose their solutions within its stated timetable in seeking to achieve an agreed solution to the notified Specialist difference or dispute.
Conciliation, mediation or other alternative dispute resolution	27.4	Where application of the Specialist Problem-Solving Hierarchy does not achieve, within its stated timetable, a solution acceptable to both the Constructor and the Specialist, and provided that neither party has by reason of that difference or dispute exercised a right of termination under clause 26, then the Constructor or the Specialist may refer such Specialist difference or dispute to conciliation in accordance with the procedure referred to in the Specialist Agreement or to mediation or any other form of alternative dispute resolution as the Constructor and the Specialist may agree.
Litigation or arbitration	27.5	Any Specialist difference or dispute that is not resolved by conciliation or any other agreed form alternative dispute resolution in accordance with clause 27.4 may be referred by the Constructor or the Specialist either to the courts stated in the Specialist Agreement or, if the Specialist Agreement so provides, to one (1) or three (3) arbitrators as stated in the Specialist Agreement who in the absence of agreement shall be appointed by the body stated in the Specialist Agreement and who shall conduct such arbitration in the location and in accordance with the rules stated in the Specialist Agreement.
Law and jurisdiction	27.6	The Specialist Contract shall be governed by the laws of the country stated in the Specialist Agreement and shall be subject to the non-exclusive jurisdiction of the courts of that country.
Limitations	27.7	Notwithstanding the method of executing the Specialist Agreement and all other Specialist Documents, the limitation period for all and any claims and proceedings

arising under or out of or in connection with the Specialist Contract or the Specialist Works shall be the period from the Specialist Completion Date stated in the Specialist Agreement. This limitation period shall not prevent claims and proceedings prior to the Specialist Completion Date or the conclusion of proceedings commenced prior to the expiry of such limitation period.

28. SPECIALIST SPECIAL TERMS

Specialist
Special
Terms

28.1 Any agreed terms amending or supplementing these Specialist Terms shall be identified as Specialist Special Terms by reference to this clause 28 and shall be set out in or attached to the Specialist Agreement.

In the Specialist Documents the following words and expressions shall have the following meanings, whether used in the singular or the plural and whatever their gender:-

Antiquity - any fossil, artefact or other object of historical interest or value which may be found on or beneath the Site;

Central Office Overheads - agreed central office overheads as distinct from Site Overheads and Profit;

Client - the party named in the Specialist Agreement to fulfil the role of Client as described in the Partnering Contract;

Client Representative - the party named in the Specialist Agreement or otherwise notified pursuant to clause 5.6 of the Specialist Terms to fulfil the role of Client Representative as described in the Partnering Contract;

Commencement Agreement - an agreement entered into between Partnering Team members pursuant to the Partnering Contract and governing commencement of the Project on Site;

Commencement Notice - a notice governing commencement of all or any stated part of the Specialist Works, signed pursuant to clause 15.1 of the Specialist Terms and based on the form set out in Part 2 of Appendix 2;

Completion Date - the date that the Project achieves Project Completion in accordance with the Partnering Contract;

Constructor - the party named in the Specialist Agreement to fulfil the role of Constructor as described in the Specialist Contract;

Consultant - any party, including the Client Representative and the Planning Supervisor, providing to the Client design or other services in relation to the Project;

Consultation - such Consultation as shall be reasonable without delaying the Specialist Works and without delaying any necessary action of any party for the benefit of the Specialist Works;

Date of Possession - the agreed date under the Partnering Contract for commencement of the Project on Site, as stated in the Commencement Agreement;

Date for Specialist Completion - the agreed date for Completion of the Specialist Works as stated in the Specialist Timetable, subject to extension in accordance with the Specialist Terms;

Design Team - the Partnering Team members named as Design Team members in or pursuant to the Partnering Contract;

Early Warning - early warning in accordance with the system described in clause 3.3 of the Specialist Terms and, if the Specialist is a Partnering Team member, the system described in clause 3.7 of the Partnering Terms;

Environment - all and any land, water and air including air within any natural or manmade structure above or below ground;

Environmental Laws - any law or statutory instrument having effect in the country in which the Site is located and any notice or requirement issued by any competent authority concerning the protection of human health or the Environment or the generation, transportation, storage, use, treatment or disposal of Hazardous Substances;

Environmental Risk Insurance - any insurance covering the consequences of environmental risks arising in relation to the Project, taken out pursuant to clause 19.5 of the Partnering Terms;

Hazardous Substances - any natural or artificial substance (whether in solid or liquid form or in the form of gas or vapour and whether alone or in combination with any substance) intrinsically capable of causing harm to man or any other living organism supported by the Environment or of damaging the Environment or public health and including but not limited to any controlled, hazardous, toxic or dangerous waste;

Intellectual Property Rights - all intellectual property rights (including, without limitation, patents, trademarks, designs, design rights, copyright, inventions, trade secrets, know-how and confidential information) and all applications for protection of any of the same;

Latent Defects Insurance - any insurance covering latent defects, taken out pursuant to clause 19.6 of the Partnering Terms;

Lead Designer - the Partnering Team member named in or pursuant to the Partnering Contract to fulfil the role of Lead Designer as described in the Partnering Contract;

Open-book - involving the declaration of all price components including Profit, Central Office Overheads, Site Overheads and the costs of materials, goods, equipment, work and services, with all and any relevant books of account, correspondence, agreements, orders, invoices, receipts and other relevant documents available for inspection;

Operation - use, occupation, operation, maintenance, repair, alteration and demolition;

Other Specialist - any party other than the Specialist providing to the Constructor (or, under clause 10.11 of the Partnering Terms, to the Client) works or services or supplies of goods, materials or equipment forming part of the Project;

Partnering Contract - the Partnering Contract referred to in the Specialist Agreement created by and between the Partnering Team members;

Partnering Team - the Partnering Team members who execute the Partnering Contract or become Partnering Team members pursuant to the Partnering Contract;

Partnering Terms - the Partnering Terms, including appendices, forming part of the Partnering Contract;

Profit - agreed gain from the Specialist Works as distinct from Central Office Overheads and Site Overheads;

Project - the Project to be designed, supplied, constructed and completed in accordance with the Partnering Contract (including all incidental activities), as described in the Partnering Contract;

Project Completion - completion of the Project in accordance with the Partnering Contract necessary for the Client to use and occupy the Project to the agreed standards;

Risk Management - a structured approach to ensure that risks are identified at the inception of the Specialist Works, that their potential impacts are allowed for and that where possible such risks or their impacts are minimised;

Site - the site of the Project including everything above and below it;

Site Overheads - agreed Site-specific overheads as distinct from Central Office Overheads and Profit;

Specialist - the party named in the Specialist Agreement to fulfil the role of Specialist as described in the Specialist Contract;

Specialist Agreement - the specialist agreement executed by the Constructor and the Specialist;

Specialist Budgets - the Constructor's monetary allowances for all or any part of the Specialist Works referred to in clause 12.4 of the Specialist Terms and stated in the Specialist Payment Terms;

Specialist Change - a change in all or any part of the Specialist Works by way of addition, omission or variation of any kind or by way of expenditure of a provisional sum identified in the Specialist Payment Terms;

Specialist Change Submission - a document to be submitted by the Specialist pursuant to clause 17.2 of the Specialist Terms, comprising its proposals as to the effect of a proposed Specialist Change;

Specialist Completion - completion of the Specialist Works in accordance with the Specialist Documents;

Specialist Completion Date - the date that the Specialist Works achieve Specialist Completion in accordance with clause 21 of the Specialist Terms;

Specialist Contract - the specialist contract created by and between the Constructor and the Specialist;

Specialist Defects Liability Period - the period following Specialist Completion during which the Specialist shall have responsibility for rectification of defects in accordance with clause 21.4 of the Specialist Terms;

Specialist Definitions - the definitions set out in this Appendix 1;

Specialist Documents - the documents governing implementation of the Specialist Works and the partnering relationship between the Constructor and the Specialist, as described in the Specialist Agreement and clause 2 of the Specialist Terms;

Specialist Final Account - the account produced by the Constructor for agreement pursuant to clause 20.12 of the Specialist Terms, showing the final balance of the Specialist Price due between the Constructor and the Specialist;

SPC INTERNATIONAL   © ACA and Trowers & Hamlins 2007

Specialist KPIs - the key performance indicators agreed between the Constructor and the Specialist for measurement of their performance in relation to the Specialist Works in accordance with clause 23 of the Specialist Terms;

Specialist Payment Terms - the payment terms referred to in clause 12 of the Specialist Terms, describing the amounts payable to the Specialist and the terms of payment;

Specialist Pre-Possession Activities - any activities forming part of the Specialist Works and undertaken by the Specialist on or off Site pursuant to a Specialist Pre-Possession Agreement;

Specialist Pre-Possession Agreement - any agreement governing Specialist Pre-Possession Activities, signed pursuant to clause 13.3 of the Specialist Terms and based on the form set out in Part 1 of Appendix 2;

Specialist Price - the agreed price payable by the Constructor to the Specialist pursuant to the Specialist Payment Terms and clause 12 of the Specialist Terms, subject to any agreed arrangements for shared savings pursuant to clause 13.2 of the Specialist Terms and subject to other increases or decreases in accordance with the Specialist Terms;

Specialist Problem-Solving Hierarchy - the arrangements for any Specialist difference or dispute to be referred within strict time limits to increasingly senior individuals representing each of the Constructor and the Specialist, as set out in the Specialist Agreement and as referred to in clause 27.3 of the Specialist Terms;

Specialist Quality Management System - the quality management system for the Specialist Works referred to in clause 16.3 of the Specialist Terms;

Specialist Retention - any amount agreed to be retained from the Specialist Price pending rectification of defects pursuant to clause 21.4 of the Specialist Terms, as specified in the Specialist Payment Terms;

Specialist Section - any section of the Specialist Works as referred to in clause 6.2 of the Specialist Terms;

Specialist Special Terms - any terms agreed to amend or supplement the Specialist Terms pursuant to clause 28 of the Specialist Terms, as set out in or attached to the Specialist Agreement;

Specialist Terms - the specialist terms, including appendices, as annexed to the Specialist Agreement;

Specialist Timetable - the timetable for implementation of the Specialist Works, as referred to in clause 6 of the Specialist Terms;

Specialist Works - the works and/or services to be implemented in accordance with the Specialist Contract (including all incidental activities), as described in the Specialist Documents;

Specialist Works Brief - the brief provided by the Constructor in relation to the Specialist Works;

Specialist Works Proposals - the proposals submitted by the Specialist for achieving the Specialist Works Brief, subject to development in accordance with the Specialist Terms;

Sub-Specialist - a party providing to the Specialist works or services or supplies of goods, materials or equipment forming part of the Specialist Works;

Sustainability - sustainability as such term may be defined in the Specialist KPIs;

Value Engineering - a structured system for the review of the design, supply and construction process to identify options and scope for improvement, including reduced capital and/or whole life costs, improved buildability and improved functionality;

Value Management - a flexible but structured management approach aimed at achieving a solution that meets the Client's needs while achieving best value;

Volume Supply Agreement - an agreement under which materials, goods or equipment are offered on preferential terms as to price, warranty, availability of parts, maintenance or otherwise;

Whole Project Insurance - any insurance covering all aspects of the Project, taken out pursuant to clause 19.7 of the Partnering Terms;

Working Day - any day other than a weekend or public holiday recognised in the country where the Site is located.

FORM OF SPECIALIST PRE-POSSESSION AGREEMENT

(see clause 13.3 of Specialist Terms)

The Constructor and the Specialist in accordance with and subject to the terms of a specialist
contract dated _____ (the "**Specialist Contract**")

made between them in relation to:-

Specialist Works: _____

Project: _____

Site: _____

Agree under this Specialist Pre-Possession Agreement that:-

1.   Words and expressions used in this Specialist Pre-Possession Agreement shall have the
       same meanings as in the Specialist Contract.

2.   The Specialist shall undertake the following Specialist Pre-Possession Activities:-

       _____

       _____

       _____

       _____

       _____

3.   The dates for completion of such Specialist Pre-Possession Activities are:-

       _____

       _____

       _____

4.   The Constructor shall pay the Specialist the following amounts for such Specialist Pre-Possession Activities:-

_____

_____

_____

_____

_____

5.   [Other terms as required]

_____

_____

_____

_____

_____

_____

_____

_____

_____

_____

Signed for and on behalf of   Signed for and on behalf of

_____   _____
(the Constructor)   (the Specialist)
by   by

_____   _____

Dated: _____   Dated: _____

SPC INTERNATIONAL   © ACA and Trowers & Hamlins 2007

SPC INTERNATIONAL

ACA SPECIALIST CONTRACT

APPENDIX 2 - PART 2

FORM OF COMMENCEMENT NOTICE

(see clause 15.1 of Specialist Terms)

The Constructor in accordance with and subject to the terms of a specialist contract dated _____ (the "**Specialist Contract**")

made between **the Constructor and the Specialist** in relation to:-

Specialist Works: _____

Project: _____

Site: _____

Gives notice to the Specialist under this Commencement Notice that:-

1.   Words and expressions used in this Commencement Notice shall have the same meanings as in the Specialist Contract.

2.   The Specialist shall commence within the period stated in the Specialist Timetable the following activities comprising all or part of the Specialist Works:-

_____

_____

_____

Signed for and on behalf of

Duplicate signed to confirm receipt for and on behalf of

_____

(the Constructor)
by

_____

(the Specialist)
by

_____

Dated: _____

_____

Dated: _____

APPENDIX 3

PART 1

INSURANCE OF PROJECT AND SITE

(see clause 19.1 of Specialist Terms)

1. The party or parties stated in the Specialist Agreement shall insure in the joint names of the Client and the Constructor and any parties stated in the Specialist Agreement (and with a waiver by the insurers of their rights of subrogation against any parties stated in the Specialist Agreement), for their full reinstatement value plus the percentage for professional fees stated in the Specialist Agreement, all work executed or in the course of execution for the purposes of the Project (including the Specialist Works) and all goods, materials and equipment on the Site or paid for pursuant to clause 20 of the Specialist Terms and all existing structures on the Site (with their contents) owned by the Client (or for which it is responsible), from the Date of Possession under the Partnering Contract until the Completion Date under the Partnering Contract, against fire, explosion, storm, tempest, flood, bursting or overflowing of water tanks, apparatus or pipes, earthquake, aircraft and other aerial devices or articles dropped from them, riot and civil commotion, theft, subsidence and heave, and any additional or adjusted risks stated in the Specialist Agreement.

2. Where so stated in the Specialist Agreement, the party stated in the Specialist Agreement shall take out and maintain from the Date of Possession under the Partnering Contract until the Completion Date under the Partnering Contract insurance in the joint names of the Client and the Constructor (and of the additional parties and with the rights of subrogation as in 1. above) for the sum stated in the Specialist Agreement against any liability, damage, loss, expense, cost, claim or proceedings suffered or incurred by the Client in respect of damage to any property (other than the Project to the extent otherwise insured) caused by collapse, subsidence, heave, vibration, weakening or removal of support or lowering of groundwater, arising out of or in connection with the implementation of the Project, except where:-

    (i)   caused by the negligence, omission or default of the Constructor or the Specialist or any Other Specialist or Consultant; or

    (ii) which could reasonably be foreseen having regard to the nature of the Project and the Site; or

    (iii) arising from a nuclear risk or war risk or sonic boom.

APPENDIX 3

PART 2

THIRD PARTY LIABILITY INSURANCE

(see clause 19.3 of Specialist Terms)

Third party liability insurance shall be taken out by the Specialist in the amount stated in the Specialist Agreement in respect of:-

1.   any liability, damage, loss, expense, cost, claim or proceedings in respect of personal injury to or death of any person arising out of or in connection with the performance of the Specialist's activities in relation to the Specialist Works and the Project whether arising on or off Site; and

2.   any liability, damage, loss, expense, cost, claim or proceedings in respect of loss, injury or damage to any property (other than the Specialist Works and any materials, goods or equipment on Site) insofar as the same is due to any negligence, omission or default of the Specialist or any individual or organisation for whom it is responsible.

APPENDIX 3

PART 3

PROFESSIONAL INDEMNITY/PRODUCT LIABILITY INSURANCE

(see clause 19.4 of Specialist Terms)

Professional indemnity insurance cover and/or product liability insurance cover shall be taken out and maintained by the Specialist if so stated in the Specialist Agreement, in the amounts (if any) stated in the Specialist Agreement, in respect of any negligence by the Specialist or any individual or organisation for whom it is responsible, (as regards professional indemnity insurance cover) in the design of any work, materials, goods or equipment forming part of or intended for the Specialist Works, or (as regards product liability insurance cover) in the design or production of any goods or equipment forming part of or intended for the Specialist Works and as to all other customary product liability risks.

SPC INTERNATIONAL   © ACA and Trowers & Hamlins 2007

APPENDIX 3

PART 4

INSURANCE - GENERAL

(see clause 19.8 of Specialist Terms)

In relation to all insurances described in clause 19 of the Specialist Terms:-

1. the insurer shall be a reputable company trading in the country in which the Site is located;

2. the insuring party shall promptly pay all premiums and whichever of the Constructor or the Specialist is the insuring party or has the right to obtain such evidence from the insuring party shall provide evidence of insurance cover, by way of copy policies or detailed certification, to the other party upon request;

3. the Constructor and the Specialist shall comply with all the terms of their respective insurance policies and shall follow all required claims procedures;

4. neither party shall knowingly do anything to invalidate any insurance cover or fail to make a claim affecting the Specialist Works or the Project or the Site or the other party if so entitled, and each party shall immediately notify the other in the event of any change of circumstances affecting any insurance cover;

5. in the event that either party is aware of a claim or potential claim, affecting the Specialist Works or the Project or the Site or the other party, then subject only to any restrictions imposed by its insurers and approved in advance by the other party, it shall immediately notify the other party of such claim or potential claim and keep the other party regularly informed as to the progress of such claim or potential claim;

6. the only permitted exclusions and deductibles shall be those that are reasonable and approved in advance by the Constructor and the Specialist.

SPC INTERNATIONAL

ACA SPECIALIST CONTRACT

APPENDIX 4

PART 1

CONCILIATION

(see clause 27.4 of Specialist Terms)

1. The term the "Conciliator" shall mean the individual named in the Specialist Agreement or (if no individual is so named) an individual to be agreed between the Constructor and the Specialist, or failing agreement within ten (10) Working Days after either party has given to the other a written request to concur in the appointment of a Conciliator, an individual to be appointed on the request of either party by the President or Vice-President for the time being of The Association of Consultant Architects Limited ("ACA").

2. If, at any time before reference of a Specialist difference or dispute to litigation or arbitration in accordance with the Specialist Terms, the Constructor and the Specialist agree to conciliation in respect of that Specialist difference or dispute, they shall apply jointly to the Conciliator who shall conduct the conciliation in accordance with the edition of the ACA Conciliation Procedure current at the date of the application.

3. Any written agreement signed by the Constructor and the Specialist, which records the terms of any settlement reached during the conciliation, shall be final and binding upon them and they shall give effect to such settlement in accordance with its terms. If either party fails to do so, then the other party shall be entitled to take legal proceedings to secure such compliance.

SPC INTERNATIONAL   © ACA and Trowers & Hamlins 2007

APPENDIX 4

PART 2

ARBITRATION (IF APPLICABLE)

(see clause 27.5 of Specialist Terms)

1. Either the Constructor or the Specialist may give notice to the other requiring that the matter be referred to arbitration in accordance with the procedure stated in the Specialist Agreement.

2. If, in the opinion of either party, any Specialist difference or dispute to be referred to arbitration under the Specialist Terms raises matters which are connected with matters raised in another Specialist difference or dispute already referred to arbitration under the Specialist Terms, the Constructor and the Specialist shall arrange for their Specialist difference or dispute to be referred to the arbitrator first appointed and such arbitration shall have the power to deal with all such connected Specialist differences or disputes as he or she thinks most just and convenient.

3. The arbitrator appointed under the Specialist Terms shall have full power to open up, review and revise any notice, decision, consent, approval, valuation, opinion or instruction of either party, and the award of such arbitrator shall be final and binding on the Constructor and the Specialist.

SPC INTERNATIONAL   © ACA and Trowers & Hamlins 2007